MONKEY THE MUMMY

David Martin ILLUSTRATED BY Scott Nash

Introduction

Before your child starts reading, read this story
description. Then look through the book together
and talk about the pictures.

This story is called *Monkey the
Mummy.* It's about how Monkey falls
again and again and Mom bandages
him more and more until Monkey
turns himself into something scary.

Monkey falls off his skateboard.

Mom bandages his leg.

Monkey falls off his bike.

Mom bandages his arm.

Monkey falls off his swing.

Mom bandages his head.

Monkey bandages himself.

Monkey is a mummy!